Coffee
Tasting Journal

Drink, Taste, Document, Log, Rate, and Evaluate
Coffee Varieties for Coffee Lovers

Nura Publishing

Printed in the United States of America

ISBN: 978-1-63540-012-0

Coffee Tasting Journal

This journal belongs to:

Coffee Tasting Journal

Today I Tasted

DATE _____

Coffee Name _____

Brand _____

Country / Region or Origin _____

Cost _____ Purchased From _____

Brew Method	Brew Time	Aroma/Taste

Would I buy again?   ☐ Yes   ☐ No

Tasting Notes

_____
_____
_____
_____
_____
_____
_____

Rating   ☆ ☆ ☆ ☆ ☆

Coffee Tasting Journal   DATE _____

Today I Tasted ☕

Coffee Name _____

Brand _____

Country / Region or Origin _____

Cost _____ Purchased From _____

Brew Method	Brew Time	Aroma/Taste

Would I buy again?   ☐ Yes   ☐ No

Tasting Notes

Rating   ☆ ☆ ☆ ☆ ☆

Coffee Tasting Journal

Today I Tasted

DATE _____

Coffee Name _____

Brand _____

Country / Region or Origin _____

Cost _____ Purchased From _____

Brew Method	Brew Time	Aroma/Taste

Would I buy again? ☐ Yes ☐ No

Tasting Notes

_____

_____

_____

_____

_____

_____

_____

Rating ☆ ☆ ☆ ☆ ☆

DATE _____

Today I Tasted ☕

Coffee Name _____

Brand _____

Country / Region or Origin _____

Cost _____ Purchased From _____

Brew Method	Brew Time	Aroma/Taste

Would I buy again? ☐ Yes ☐ No

Tasting Notes

_____

_____

_____

_____

_____

_____

Rating ☆ ☆ ☆ ☆ ☆

Coffee Tasting Journal

Today I Tasted

DATE _____

Coffee Name _____

Brand _____

Country / Region or Origin _____

Cost _____ Purchased From _____

Brew Method	Brew Time	Aroma/Taste

Would I buy again? ☐ Yes ☐ No

Tasting Notes

Rating ☆ ☆ ☆ ☆ ☆

Coffee Tasting Journal

DATE _____

Today I Tasted ☕

Coffee Name _____

Brand _____

Country / Region or Origin _____

Cost _____ Purchased From _____

Brew Method	Brew Time	Aroma/Taste

Would I buy again? ☐ Yes ☐ No

Tasting Notes

Rating ☆ ☆ ☆ ☆ ☆

Coffee Tasting Journal

Today I Tasted ☕

DATE _____

Coffee Name _____

Brand _____

Country / Region or Origin _____

Cost _____ Purchased From _____

Brew Method	Brew Time	Aroma/Taste

Would I buy again?   ☐ Yes   ☐ No

Tasting Notes

_____

_____

_____

_____

_____

_____

_____

Rating   ☆ ☆ ☆ ☆ ☆

DATE _____

Today I Tasted ☕

Coffee Name _____

Brand _____

Country / Region or Origin _____

Cost _____ Purchased From _____

Brew Method	Brew Time	Aroma/Taste

Would I buy again? ☐ Yes ☐ No

Tasting Notes

_____

_____

_____

_____

_____

_____

_____

Rating ☆ ☆ ☆ ☆ ☆

Coffee Tasting Journal

Today I Tasted

DATE _____

Coffee Name _____

Brand _____

Country / Region or Origin _____

Cost _____ Purchased From _____

Brew Method	Brew Time	Aroma/Taste

Would I buy again? ☐ Yes ☐ No

Tasting Notes

_____

_____

_____

_____

_____

_____

_____

Rating ☆ ☆ ☆ ☆ ☆

Coffee Tasting Journal

Today I Tasted ☕

DATE _____

Coffee Name _____

Brand _____

Country / Region or Origin _____

Cost _____ Purchased From _____

Brew Method	Brew Time	Aroma/Taste

Would I buy again?   ☐ Yes   ☐ No

Tasting Notes

Rating ☆ ☆ ☆ ☆ ☆

Coffee Tasting Journal

DATE _____

Today I Tasted ☕

Coffee Name _____

Brand _____

Country / Region or Origin _____

Cost _____ Purchased From _____

Brew Method	Brew Time	Aroma/Taste

Would I buy again?　　☐ Yes　　☐ No

Tasting Notes

Rating　☆ ☆ ☆ ☆ ☆

DATE _____

Today I Tasted ☕

Coffee Name _____

Brand _____

Country / Region or Origin _____

Cost _____ Purchased From _____

Brew Method	Brew Time	Aroma/Taste

Would I buy again? ☐ Yes   ☐ No

Tasting Notes

Rating ☆ ☆ ☆ ☆ ☆

Coffee Tasting Journal

DATE _____

Today I Tasted ☕

Coffee Name _____

Brand _____

Country / Region or Origin _____

Cost _____ Purchased From _____

Brew Method	Brew Time	Aroma/Taste

Would I buy again? ☐ Yes ☐ No

Tasting Notes

_____
_____
_____
_____
_____
_____
_____

Rating ☆ ☆ ☆ ☆ ☆

Coffee Tasting Journal

Today I Tasted

DATE _____

Coffee Name _____

Brand _____

Country / Region or Origin _____

Cost _____ Purchased From _____

Brew Method	Brew Time	Aroma/Taste

Would I buy again? ☐ Yes ☐ No

Tasting Notes

_____
_____
_____
_____
_____
_____
_____

Rating ☆ ☆ ☆ ☆ ☆

Coffee Tasting Journal

DATE _____

Today I Tasted ☕

Coffee Name _____

Brand _____

Country / Region or Origin _____

Cost _____ Purchased From _____

Brew Method	Brew Time	Aroma/Taste

Would I buy again? ☐ Yes ☐ No

Tasting Notes

Rating ☆ ☆ ☆ ☆ ☆

Coffee Tasting Journal

DATE _____

Today I Tasted ☕

Coffee Name _____

Brand _____

Country / Region or Origin _____

Cost _____ Purchased From _____

Brew Method	Brew Time	Aroma/Taste

Would I buy again? ☐ Yes ☐ No

Tasting Notes

_____

_____

_____

_____

_____

_____

_____

Rating ☆ ☆ ☆ ☆ ☆

Coffee Tasting Journal

Today I Tasted

DATE _____

Coffee Name _____

Brand _____

Country / Region or Origin _____

Cost _____ Purchased From _____

Brew Method	Brew Time	Aroma/Taste

Would I buy again? ☐ Yes ☐ No

Tasting Notes

_____

_____

_____

_____

_____

_____

_____

Rating ☆ ☆ ☆ ☆ ☆

DATE _____

Today I Tasted ☕

Coffee Name _____

Brand _____

Country / Region or Origin _____

Cost _____ Purchased From _____

Brew Method	Brew Time	Aroma/Taste

Would I buy again? ☐ Yes ☐ No

Tasting Notes

_____

_____

_____

_____

_____

_____

_____

Rating ☆ ☆ ☆ ☆ ☆

Coffee Tasting Journal

DATE _____

Today I Tasted ☕

Coffee Name _____

Brand _____

Country / Region or Origin _____

Cost _____ Purchased From _____

Brew Method	Brew Time	Aroma/Taste

Would I buy again?   ☐ Yes   ☐ No

Tasting Notes

_____

_____

_____

_____

_____

_____

_____

Rating ☆ ☆ ☆ ☆ ☆

Coffee Tasting Journal

Today I Tasted ☕

DATE _____

Coffee Name _____

Brand _____

Country / Region or Origin _____

Cost _____ Purchased From _____

Brew Method	Brew Time	Aroma/Taste

Would I buy again? ☐ Yes ☐ No

Tasting Notes

Rating ☆ ☆ ☆ ☆ ☆

Coffee Tasting Journal

Today I Tasted ☕

DATE _____

Coffee Name _____

Brand _____

Country / Region or Origin _____

Cost _____ Purchased From _____

Brew Method	Brew Time	Aroma/Taste

Would I buy again?   ☐ Yes   ☐ No

Tasting Notes

_____
_____
_____
_____
_____
_____
_____

Rating ☆ ☆ ☆ ☆ ☆

Coffee Tasting Journal   DATE _____

Today I Tasted ☕

Coffee Name _____

Brand _____

Country / Region or Origin _____

Cost _____ Purchased From _____

Brew Method	Brew Time	Aroma/Taste

Would I buy again?   ☐ Yes   ☐ No

Tasting Notes

Rating ☆ ☆ ☆ ☆ ☆

Coffee Tasting Journal

Today I Tasted

DATE _____

Coffee Name _____

Brand _____

Country / Region or Origin _____

Cost _____ Purchased From _____

Brew Method	Brew Time	Aroma/Taste

Would I buy again?   ☐ Yes   ☐ No

Tasting Notes

_____

_____

_____

_____

_____

_____

Rating   ☆ ☆ ☆ ☆ ☆

Coffee Tasting Journal

DATE _____

Today I Tasted ☕

Coffee Name _____

Brand _____

Country / Region or Origin _____

Cost _____ Purchased From _____

Brew Method	Brew Time	Aroma/Taste

Would I buy again? ☐ Yes ☐ No

Tasting Notes

Rating ☆ ☆ ☆ ☆ ☆

Coffee Tasting Journal

DATE _____

Today I Tasted ☕

Coffee Name _____

Brand _____

Country / Region or Origin _____

Cost _____ Purchased From _____

Brew Method	Brew Time	Aroma/Taste

Would I buy again?   ☐ Yes   ☐ No

Tasting Notes

Rating   ☆ ☆ ☆ ☆ ☆

DATE _____

Today I Tasted ☕

Coffee Name _____

Brand _____

Country / Region or Origin _____

Cost _____ Purchased From _____

Brew Method	Brew Time	Aroma/Taste

Would I buy again? ☐ Yes ☐ No

Tasting Notes

_____

_____

_____

_____

_____

_____

_____

Rating ☆ ☆ ☆ ☆ ☆

Coffee Tasting Journal

DATE _____

Today I Tasted ☕

Coffee Name _____

Brand _____

Country / Region or Origin _____

Cost _____ Purchased From _____

Brew Method	Brew Time	Aroma/Taste

Would I buy again? ☐ Yes   ☐ No

Tasting Notes

_____
_____
_____
_____
_____
_____

Rating ☆ ☆ ☆ ☆ ☆

Coffee Tasting Journal   DATE _____

Today I Tasted ☕

Coffee Name _____

Brand _____

Country / Region or Origin _____

Cost _____ Purchased From _____

Brew Method	Brew Time	Aroma/Taste

Would I buy again?   ☐ Yes   ☐ No

Tasting Notes

_____

_____

_____

_____

_____

_____

Rating ☆ ☆ ☆ ☆ ☆

Coffee Tasting Journal

Today I Tasted

Coffee Name _____

Brand _____

Country / Region or Origin _____

Cost _____ Purchased From _____

Brew Method	Brew Time	Aroma/Taste

Would I buy again?   ☐ Yes   ☐ No

Tasting Notes

_____

_____

_____

_____

_____

_____

_____

Rating   ☆ ☆ ☆ ☆ ☆

Coffee Tasting Journal

DATE _____

Today I Tasted ☕

Coffee Name _____

Brand _____

Country / Region or Origin _____

Cost _____ Purchased From _____

Brew Method	Brew Time	Aroma/Taste

Would I buy again? ☐ Yes   ☐ No

Tasting Notes

Rating ☆ ☆ ☆ ☆ ☆

Coffee Tasting Journal

Today I Tasted ☕

Coffee Name _____

Brand _____

Country / Region or Origin _____

Cost _____ Purchased From _____

Brew Method	Brew Time	Aroma/Taste

Would I buy again?   ☐ Yes   ☐ No

Tasting Notes

_____

_____

_____

_____

_____

_____

Rating   ☆ ☆ ☆ ☆ ☆

Coffee Tasting Journal

Today I Tasted ☕

Coffee Name _____

Brand _____

Country / Region or Origin _____

Cost _____ Purchased From _____

Brew Method	Brew Time	Aroma/Taste

Would I buy again? ☐ Yes ☐ No

Tasting Notes
_____
_____
_____
_____
_____
_____

Rating ☆ ☆ ☆ ☆ ☆

Coffee Tasting Journal

Today I Tasted

DATE _____

Coffee Name _____

Brand _____

Country / Region or Origin _____

Cost _____ Purchased From _____

Brew Method	Brew Time	Aroma/Taste

Would I buy again?   ☐ Yes   ☐ No

Tasting Notes

Rating ☆ ☆ ☆ ☆ ☆

Coffee Tasting Journal

DATE _____

Today I Tasted ☕

Coffee Name _____

Brand _____

Country / Region or Origin _____

Cost _____ Purchased From _____

Brew Method	Brew Time	Aroma/Taste

Would I buy again?   ☐ Yes   ☐ No

Tasting Notes
_____
_____
_____
_____
_____
_____

Rating ☆ ☆ ☆ ☆ ☆

Coffee Tasting Journal

Today I Tasted ☕

DATE _____

Coffee Name _____

Brand _____

Country / Region or Origin _____

Cost _____ Purchased From _____

Brew Method	Brew Time	Aroma/Taste

Would I buy again?　□ Yes　□ No

Tasting Notes

_____

_____

_____

_____

_____

_____

_____

Rating　☆ ☆ ☆ ☆ ☆

Coffee Tasting Journal

Today I Tasted ☕

Coffee Name _____

Brand _____

Country / Region or Origin _____

Cost _____ Purchased From _____

Brew Method	Brew Time	Aroma/Taste

Would I buy again?　☐ Yes　☐ No

Tasting Notes

_____

_____

_____

_____

_____

_____

Rating　☆ ☆ ☆ ☆ ☆

Coffee Tasting Journal

DATE _____

Today I Tasted ☕

Coffee Name _____

Brand _____

Country / Region or Origin _____

Cost _____ Purchased From _____

Brew Method	Brew Time	Aroma/Taste

Would I buy again? ☐ Yes ☐ No

Tasting Notes

_____

_____

_____

_____

_____

_____

Rating ☆ ☆ ☆ ☆ ☆

DATE _____

Today I Tasted ☕

Coffee Name _____

Brand _____

Country / Region or Origin _____

Cost _____ Purchased From _____

Brew Method	Brew Time	Aroma/Taste

Would I buy again? ☐ Yes   ☐ No

Tasting Notes

_____

_____

_____

_____

_____

_____

Rating ☆ ☆ ☆ ☆ ☆

Coffee Tasting Journal

Today I Tasted

DATE _____

Coffee Name _____

Brand _____

Country / Region or Origin _____

Cost _____ Purchased From _____

Brew Method	Brew Time	Aroma/Taste

Would I buy again? ☐ Yes ☐ No

Tasting Notes

_____

_____

_____

_____

_____

_____

Rating ☆ ☆ ☆ ☆ ☆

Coffee Tasting Journal

DATE _____

Today I Tasted ☕

Coffee Name _____

Brand _____

Country / Region or Origin _____

Cost _____ Purchased From _____

Brew Method	Brew Time	Aroma/Taste

Would I buy again?   ☐ Yes   ☐ No

Tasting Notes

Rating ☆ ☆ ☆ ☆ ☆

Coffee Tasting Journal

Today I Tasted ☕

DATE _____

Coffee Name _____

Brand _____

Country / Region or Origin _____

Cost _____ Purchased From _____

Brew Method	Brew Time	Aroma/Taste

Would I buy again? ☐ Yes ☐ No

Tasting Notes

_____
_____
_____
_____
_____
_____
_____

Rating ☆ ☆ ☆ ☆ ☆

Coffee Tasting Journal   DATE _____

Today I Tasted ☕

Coffee Name _____

Brand _____

Country / Region or Origin _____

Cost _____ Purchased From _____

Brew Method	Brew Time	Aroma/Taste

Would I buy again?   ☐ Yes   ☐ No

Tasting Notes

Rating ☆ ☆ ☆ ☆ ☆

Coffee Tasting Journal

Today I Tasted ☕

DATE _____

Coffee Name _____

Brand _____

Country / Region or Origin _____

Cost _____ Purchased From _____

Brew Method	Brew Time	Aroma/Taste

Would I buy again? ☐ Yes ☐ No

Tasting Notes

Rating ☆ ☆ ☆ ☆ ☆

Coffee Tasting Journal

DATE _____

Today I Tasted ☕

Coffee Name _____

Brand _____

Country / Region or Origin _____

Cost _____ Purchased From _____

Brew Method	Brew Time	Aroma/Taste

Would I buy again? ☐ Yes ☐ No

Tasting Notes

Rating ☆ ☆ ☆ ☆ ☆

Coffee Tasting Journal

Today I Tasted ☕

DATE _____

Coffee Name _____

Brand _____

Country / Region or Origin _____

Cost _____ Purchased From _____

Brew Method	Brew Time	Aroma/Taste

Would I buy again?   ☐ Yes   ☐ No

Tasting Notes

Rating ☆ ☆ ☆ ☆ ☆

Coffee Tasting Journal

Today I Tasted ☕

DATE _____

Coffee Name _____

Brand _____

Country / Region or Origin _____

Cost _____ Purchased From _____

Brew Method	Brew Time	Aroma/Taste

Would I buy again?   ☐ Yes   ☐ No

Tasting Notes

Rating ☆ ☆ ☆ ☆ ☆

Coffee Tasting Journal

Today I Tasted

DATE _____

Coffee Name _____

Brand _____

Country / Region or Origin _____

Cost _____ Purchased From _____

Brew Method	Brew Time	Aroma/Taste

Would I buy again? ☐ Yes ☐ No

Tasting Notes

Rating ☆ ☆ ☆ ☆ ☆

Coffee Tasting Journal

DATE _____

Today I Tasted ☕

Coffee Name _____

Brand _____

Country / Region or Origin _____

Cost _____ Purchased From _____

Brew Method	Brew Time	Aroma/Taste

Would I buy again?   ☐ Yes   ☐ No

Tasting Notes

Rating ☆ ☆ ☆ ☆ ☆

Coffee Tasting Journal

Today I Tasted ☕

DATE _____

Coffee Name _____

Brand _____

Country / Region or Origin _____

Cost _____ Purchased From _____

Brew Method	Brew Time	Aroma/Taste

Would I buy again? ☐ Yes ☐ No

Tasting Notes

_____

_____

_____

_____

_____

_____

_____

Rating ☆ ☆ ☆ ☆ ☆

Coffee Tasting Journal   DATE _____

Today I Tasted

Coffee Name _____

Brand _____

Country / Region or Origin _____

Cost _____ Purchased From _____

Brew Method	Brew Time	Aroma/Taste

Would I buy again?   ☐ Yes   ☐ No

Tasting Notes

Rating   ☆ ☆ ☆ ☆ ☆

DATE _____

Today I Tasted ☕

Coffee Name _____

Brand _____

Country / Region or Origin _____

Cost _____ Purchased From _____

Brew Method	Brew Time	Aroma/Taste

Would I buy again? ☐ Yes ☐ No

Tasting Notes

Rating ☆ ☆ ☆ ☆ ☆

Coffee Tasting Journal

DATE _____

Today I Tasted

Coffee Name _____

Brand _____

Country / Region or Origin _____

Cost _____ Purchased From _____

Brew Method	Brew Time	Aroma/Taste

Would I buy again? ☐ Yes ☐ No

Tasting Notes

Rating ☆ ☆ ☆ ☆ ☆

Coffee Tasting Journal

Today I Tasted ☕

DATE _____

Coffee Name _____

Brand _____

Country / Region or Origin _____

Cost _____ Purchased From _____

Brew Method	Brew Time	Aroma/Taste

Would I buy again? ☐ Yes ☐ No

Tasting Notes

Rating ☆ ☆ ☆ ☆ ☆

Coffee Tasting Journal   DATE _____

Today I Tasted ☕

Coffee Name _____

Brand _____

Country / Region or Origin _____

Cost _____ Purchased From _____

Brew Method	Brew Time	Aroma/Taste

Would I buy again?   ☐ Yes   ☐ No

Tasting Notes

Rating   ☆ ☆ ☆ ☆ ☆

Coffee Tasting Journal

Today I Tasted

DATE _____

Coffee Name _____

Brand _____

Country / Region or Origin _____

Cost _____ Purchased From _____

Brew Method	Brew Time	Aroma/Taste

Would I buy again? ☐ Yes   ☐ No

Tasting Notes

Rating ☆ ☆ ☆ ☆ ☆

Coffee Tasting Journal

DATE _____

Today I Tasted ☕

Coffee Name _____

Brand _____

Country / Region or Origin _____

Cost _____ Purchased From _____

Brew Method	Brew Time	Aroma/Taste

Would I buy again? ☐ Yes ☐ No

Tasting Notes

_____

_____

_____

_____

_____

_____

Rating ☆ ☆ ☆ ☆ ☆

Coffee Tasting Journal

Today I Tasted ☕

DATE _____

Coffee Name _____

Brand _____

Country / Region or Origin _____

Cost _____ Purchased From _____

Brew Method	Brew Time	Aroma/Taste

Would I buy again?   ☐ Yes   ☐ No

Tasting Notes

_____

_____

_____

_____

_____

_____

Rating   ☆ ☆ ☆ ☆ ☆

Coffee Tasting Journal

Today I Tasted

DATE _____

Coffee Name _____

Brand _____

Country / Region or Origin _____

Cost _____ Purchased From _____

Brew Method	Brew Time	Aroma/Taste

Would I buy again? ☐ Yes ☐ No

Tasting Notes

_____

_____

_____

_____

_____

_____

Rating ☆ ☆ ☆ ☆ ☆

Coffee Tasting Journal

Today I Tasted ☕

Coffee Name _____

Brand _____

Country / Region or Origin _____

Cost _____ Purchased From _____

Brew Method	Brew Time	Aroma/Taste

Would I buy again? ☐ Yes ☐ No

Tasting Notes

_____
_____
_____
_____
_____
_____
_____

Rating ☆ ☆ ☆ ☆ ☆

Coffee Tasting Journal

Today I Tasted

DATE _____

Coffee Name _____

Brand _____

Country / Region or Origin _____

Cost _____ Purchased From _____

Brew Method	Brew Time	Aroma/Taste

Would I buy again? ☐ Yes   ☐ No

Tasting Notes

Rating ☆ ☆ ☆ ☆ ☆

Coffee Tasting Journal

DATE _____

Today I Tasted

Coffee Name _____

Brand _____

Country / Region or Origin _____

Cost _____ Purchased From _____

Brew Method	Brew Time	Aroma/Taste

Would I buy again?   ☐ Yes   ☐ No

Tasting Notes

_____
_____
_____
_____
_____
_____
_____

Rating ☆ ☆ ☆ ☆ ☆

Coffee Tasting Journal   DATE _____

Today I Tasted

Coffee Name _____

Brand _____

Country / Region or Origin _____

Cost _____ Purchased From _____

Brew Method	Brew Time	Aroma/Taste

Would I buy again?   ☐ Yes   ☐ No

Tasting Notes

Rating   ☆ ☆ ☆ ☆ ☆

Coffee Tasting Journal

DATE _____

Today I Tasted ☕

Coffee Name _____

Brand _____

Country / Region or Origin _____

Cost _____ Purchased From _____

Brew Method	Brew Time	Aroma/Taste

Would I buy again? ☐ Yes ☐ No

Tasting Notes

Rating ☆ ☆ ☆ ☆ ☆

Coffee Tasting Journal   DATE _____

Today I Tasted ☕

Coffee Name _____

Brand _____

Country / Region or Origin _____

Cost _____ Purchased From _____

Brew Method	Brew Time	Aroma/Taste

Would I buy again?   ☐ Yes   ☐ No

Tasting Notes

Rating   ☆ ☆ ☆ ☆ ☆

Coffee Tasting Journal

DATE _____

Today I Tasted ☕

Coffee Name _____

Brand _____

Country / Region or Origin _____

Cost _____ Purchased From _____

Brew Method	Brew Time	Aroma/Taste

Would I buy again? ☐ Yes ☐ No

Tasting Notes

Rating ☆ ☆ ☆ ☆ ☆

Coffee Tasting Journal

DATE _____

Today I Tasted

Coffee Name _____

Brand _____

Country / Region or Origin _____

Cost _____ Purchased From _____

Brew Method	Brew Time	Aroma/Taste

Would I buy again?   ☐ Yes   ☐ No

Tasting Notes

Rating   ☆ ☆ ☆ ☆ ☆

Coffee Tasting Journal

Today I Tasted ☕

Coffee Name _____

Brand _____

Country / Region or Origin _____

Cost _____ Purchased From _____

Brew Method	Brew Time	Aroma/Taste

Would I buy again? ☐ Yes   ☐ No

Tasting Notes

_____

_____

_____

_____

_____

_____

_____

Rating ☆ ☆ ☆ ☆ ☆

Coffee Tasting Journal

DATE _____

Today I Tasted

Coffee Name _____

Brand _____

Country / Region or Origin _____

Cost _____ Purchased From _____

Brew Method	Brew Time	Aroma/Taste

Would I buy again?　☐ Yes　☐ No

Tasting Notes

Rating　☆ ☆ ☆ ☆ ☆

Coffee Tasting Journal

Today I Tasted ☕

DATE _____

Coffee Name _____

Brand _____

Country / Region or Origin _____

Cost _____ Purchased From _____

Brew Method	Brew Time	Aroma/Taste

Would I buy again? ☐ Yes   ☐ No

Tasting Notes

Rating ☆ ☆ ☆ ☆ ☆

Coffee Tasting Journal

DATE _____

Today I Tasted ☕

Coffee Name _____

Brand _____

Country / Region or Origin _____

Cost _____ Purchased From _____

Brew Method	Brew Time	Aroma/Taste

Would I buy again?   ☐ Yes   ☐ No

Tasting Notes
_____
_____
_____
_____
_____
_____

Rating ☆ ☆ ☆ ☆ ☆

Coffee Tasting Journal

DATE _____

Today I Tasted ☕

Coffee Name _____

Brand _____

Country / Region or Origin _____

Cost _____ Purchased From _____

Brew Method	Brew Time	Aroma/Taste

Would I buy again? ☐ Yes   ☐ No

Tasting Notes

Rating ☆ ☆ ☆ ☆ ☆

Coffee Tasting Journal

DATE _____

Today I Tasted

Coffee Name _____

Brand _____

Country / Region or Origin _____

Cost _____ Purchased From _____

Brew Method	Brew Time	Aroma/Taste

Would I buy again? ☐ Yes ☐ No

Tasting Notes

Rating ☆ ☆ ☆ ☆ ☆

Coffee Tasting Journal

Today I Tasted ☕

DATE _____

Coffee Name _____

Brand _____

Country / Region or Origin _____

Cost _____ Purchased From _____

Brew Method	Brew Time	Aroma/Taste

Would I buy again? ☐ Yes ☐ No

Tasting Notes

Rating ☆ ☆ ☆ ☆ ☆

Coffee Tasting Journal   DATE _____

Today 1 Tasted ☕

Coffee Name _____

Brand _____

Country / Region or Origin _____

Cost _____ Purchased From _____

Brew Method	Brew Time	Aroma/Taste

Would 1 buy again?   ☐ Yes   ☐ No

Tasting Notes

Rating ☆ ☆ ☆ ☆ ☆

Coffee Tasting Journal   DATE _____

Today I Tasted ☕

Coffee Name _____

Brand _____

Country / Region or Origin _____

Cost _____ Purchased From _____

Brew Method	Brew Time	Aroma/Taste

Would I buy again?   ☐ Yes   ☐ No

Tasting Notes

Rating ☆ ☆ ☆ ☆ ☆

Coffee Tasting Journal

DATE _____

Today I Tasted ☕

Coffee Name _____

Brand _____

Country / Region or Origin _____

Cost _____ Purchased From _____

Brew Method	Brew Time	Aroma/Taste

Would I buy again?   ☐ Yes   ☐ No

Tasting Notes

Rating ☆ ☆ ☆ ☆ ☆

Coffee Tasting Journal

Today I Tasted

DATE _____

Coffee Name _____

Brand _____

Country / Region or Origin _____

Cost _____ Purchased From _____

Brew Method	Brew Time	Aroma/Taste

Would I buy again? ☐ Yes ☐ No

Tasting Notes

_____

_____

_____

_____

_____

_____

_____

Rating ☆ ☆ ☆ ☆ ☆

Coffee Tasting Journal   DATE _____

Today I Tasted ☕

Coffee Name _____

Brand _____

Country / Region or Origin _____

Cost _____ Purchased From _____

Brew Method	Brew Time	Aroma/Taste

Would I buy again?   ☐ Yes   ☐ No

Tasting Notes

_____

_____

_____

_____

_____

_____

Rating   ☆ ☆ ☆ ☆ ☆

Coffee Tasting Journal

DATE _____

Today I Tasted ☕

Coffee Name _____

Brand _____

Country / Region or Origin _____

Cost _____ Purchased From _____

Brew Method	Brew Time	Aroma/Taste

Would I buy again? ☐ Yes   ☐ No

Tasting Notes

Rating ☆ ☆ ☆ ☆ ☆

Coffee Tasting Journal

DATE _____

Today I Tasted ☕

Coffee Name _____

Brand _____

Country / Region or Origin _____

Cost _____ Purchased From _____

Brew Method	Brew Time	Aroma/Taste

Would I buy again? ☐ Yes   ☐ No

Tasting Notes

Rating ☆ ☆ ☆ ☆ ☆

Coffee Tasting Journal

DATE _____

Today I Tasted ☕

Coffee Name _____

Brand _____

Country / Region or Origin _____

Cost _____ Purchased From _____

Brew Method	Brew Time	Aroma/Taste

Would I buy again?　　☐ Yes　　☐ No

Tasting Notes

Rating　☆ ☆ ☆ ☆ ☆

Coffee Tasting Journal

Today I Tasted

Coffee Name _____

Brand _____

Country / Region or Origin _____

Cost _____ Purchased From _____

Brew Method	Brew Time	Aroma/Taste

Would I buy again? ☐ Yes ☐ No

Tasting Notes

Rating ☆ ☆ ☆ ☆ ☆

Coffee Tasting Journal

Today I Tasted

DATE _____

Coffee Name _____

Brand _____

Country / Region or Origin _____

Cost _____ Purchased From _____

Brew Method	Brew Time	Aroma/Taste

Would I buy again? ☐ Yes ☐ No

Tasting Notes

Rating ☆ ☆ ☆ ☆ ☆

Coffee Tasting Journal

DATE _____

Today I Tasted ☕

Coffee Name _____

Brand _____

Country / Region or Origin _____

Cost _____ Purchased From _____

Brew Method	Brew Time	Aroma/Taste

Would I buy again? ☐ Yes ☐ No

Tasting Notes

Rating ☆ ☆ ☆ ☆ ☆

Coffee Tasting Journal

DATE _____

Today I Tasted ☕

Coffee Name _____

Brand _____

Country / Region or Origin _____

Cost _____ Purchased From _____

Brew Method	Brew Time	Aroma/Taste

Would I buy again? ☐ Yes   ☐ No

Tasting Notes

Rating ☆ ☆ ☆ ☆ ☆

Coffee Tasting Journal

DATE _____

Today I Tasted ☕

Coffee Name _____

Brand _____

Country / Region or Origin _____

Cost _____ Purchased From _____

Brew Method	Brew Time	Aroma/Taste

Would I buy again? ☐ Yes ☐ No

Tasting Notes

Rating ☆ ☆ ☆ ☆ ☆

Coffee Tasting Journal

DATE _____

Today I Tasted

Coffee Name _____

Brand _____

Country / Region or Origin _____

Cost _____ Purchased From _____

Brew Method	Brew Time	Aroma/Taste

Would I buy again? ☐ Yes ☐ No

Tasting Notes

_____
_____
_____
_____
_____
_____
_____

Rating ☆ ☆ ☆ ☆ ☆

Coffee Tasting Journal

Today I Tasted

Coffee Name _____

Brand _____

Country / Region or Origin _____

Cost _____ Purchased From _____

Brew Method	Brew Time	Aroma/Taste

Would I buy again? ☐ Yes ☐ No

Tasting Notes

Rating ☆ ☆ ☆ ☆ ☆

Coffee Tasting Journal

Today I Tasted

DATE _____

Coffee Name _____

Brand _____

Country / Region or Origin _____

Cost _____ Purchased From _____

Brew Method	Brew Time	Aroma/Taste

Would I buy again? ☐ Yes   ☐ No

Tasting Notes

_____

_____

_____

_____

_____

_____

_____

Rating   ☆ ☆ ☆ ☆ ☆

Coffee Tasting Journal

Today I Tasted ☕

DATE _____

Coffee Name _____

Brand _____

Country / Region or Origin _____

Cost _____ Purchased From _____

Brew Method	Brew Time	Aroma/Taste

Would I buy again?   ☐ Yes   ☐ No

Tasting Notes

Rating ☆ ☆ ☆ ☆ ☆

Coffee Tasting Journal

Today I Tasted ☕

Coffee Name _____

Brand _____

Country / Region or Origin _____

Cost _____ Purchased From _____

Brew Method	Brew Time	Aroma/Taste

Would I buy again? ☐ Yes   ☐ No

Tasting Notes

_____

_____

_____

_____

_____

_____

_____

Rating ☆ ☆ ☆ ☆ ☆

Coffee Tasting Journal

DATE _____

Today I Tasted ☕

Coffee Name _____

Brand _____

Country / Region or Origin _____

Cost _____ Purchased From _____

Brew Method	Brew Time	Aroma/Taste

Would I buy again?   ☐ Yes   ☐ No

Tasting Notes

Rating ☆ ☆ ☆ ☆ ☆

Coffee Tasting Journal

Today I Tasted ☕

DATE _____

Coffee Name _____

Brand _____

Country / Region or Origin _____

Cost _____ Purchased From _____

Brew Method	Brew Time	Aroma/Taste

Would I buy again? ☐ Yes   ☐ No

Tasting Notes

Rating ☆ ☆ ☆ ☆ ☆

Coffee Tasting Journal

DATE _____

Today I Tasted ☕

Coffee Name _____

Brand _____

Country / Region or Origin _____

Cost _____ Purchased From _____

Brew Method	Brew Time	Aroma/Taste

Would I buy again? ☐ Yes   ☐ No

Tasting Notes

Rating ☆ ☆ ☆ ☆ ☆

Coffee Tasting Journal

DATE _____

Today I Tasted ☕

Coffee Name _____

Brand _____

Country / Region or Origin _____

Cost _____ Purchased From _____

Brew Method	Brew Time	Aroma/Taste

Would I buy again? ☐ Yes   ☐ No

Tasting Notes

Rating ☆ ☆ ☆ ☆ ☆

Coffee Tasting Journal   DATE _____

Today I Tasted ☕

Coffee Name _____

Brand _____

Country / Region or Origin _____

Cost _____ Purchased From _____

Brew Method	Brew Time	Aroma/Taste

Would I buy again?   ☐ Yes   ☐ No

Tasting Notes
_____
_____
_____
_____
_____
_____

Rating ☆ ☆ ☆ ☆ ☆

Coffee Tasting Journal

DATE _____

Today I Tasted ☕

Coffee Name _____

Brand _____

Country / Region or Origin _____

Cost _____ Purchased From _____

Brew Method	Brew Time	Aroma/Taste

Would I buy again? ☐ Yes   ☐ No

Tasting Notes

_____

_____

_____

_____

_____

_____

_____

Rating ☆ ☆ ☆ ☆ ☆

Coffee Tasting Journal

DATE _____

Today I Tasted ☕

Coffee Name _____

Brand _____

Country / Region or Origin _____

Cost _____ Purchased From _____

Brew Method	Brew Time	Aroma/Taste

Would I buy again? ☐ Yes ☐ No

Tasting Notes

Rating ☆ ☆ ☆ ☆ ☆

Coffee Tasting Journal

DATE _____

Today I Tasted ☕

Coffee Name _____

Brand _____

Country / Region or Origin _____

Cost _____ Purchased From _____

Brew Method	Brew Time	Aroma/Taste

Would I buy again?   ☐ Yes   ☐ No

Tasting Notes

Rating   ☆ ☆ ☆ ☆ ☆

Coffee Tasting Journal

Today I Tasted ☕

Coffee Name _____

Brand _____

Country / Region or Origin _____

Cost _____ Purchased From _____

Brew Method	Brew Time	Aroma/Taste

Would I buy again? ☐ Yes ☐ No

Tasting Notes

Rating ☆ ☆ ☆ ☆ ☆

Coffee Tasting Journal

Today I Tasted ☕

DATE _____

Coffee Name _____

Brand _____

Country / Region or Origin _____

Cost _____ Purchased From _____

Brew Method	Brew Time	Aroma/Taste

Would I buy again? ☐ Yes ☐ No

Tasting Notes

_____

_____

_____

_____

_____

_____

Rating ☆ ☆ ☆ ☆ ☆

Coffee Tasting Journal

DATE _____

Today I Tasted

Coffee Name _____

Brand _____

Country / Region or Origin _____

Cost _____ Purchased From _____

Brew Method	Brew Time	Aroma/Taste

Would I buy again?   ☐ Yes   ☐ No

Tasting Notes

Rating ☆ ☆ ☆ ☆ ☆

Made in the USA
Middletown, DE
23 February 2022

61715058R00062